Kevin can see a
big cat.

The big cat can
run  fast.

Kevin cannot run

fast.

The big cat can run

zig-zag, zig-zag.

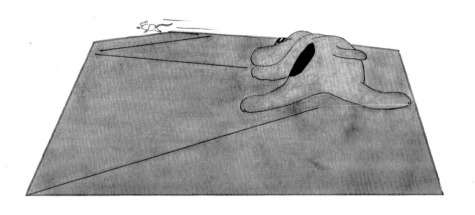

Kevin cannot run

zig-zag, zig-zag.

The big cat runs

into a big box.

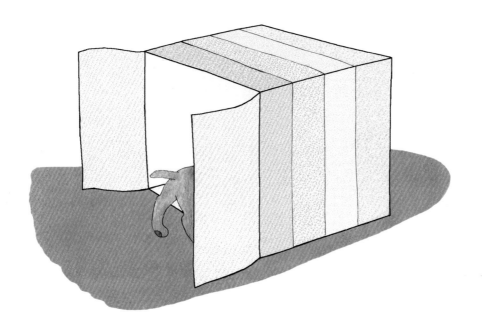

Kevin runs into a big box.

Look at Kevin and
the big cat in the
big box.